CONTENTS

Introduction	i
A Trip to the Zoo	1
Legs, Feet, and Toes	2
Dr. Doomuch's Pet Supplies	3
Sweet Dreams	4
Bean's Story	5
Vegetables, Fruits, and Vegetable-Fruits	6
Harborside Aquarium	7
Tooth Totals	8
Birth of a Butterfly	9
Moving Up	10
Big Ocean Animals	11
Class Pet	12
Snake Facts	13
The One Minute Race	14
Keep Track of the Animal Tracks	15
Food for a Giant	16
Tree Time	17
Free Ride	18
Barry Brontosaurus and His Friends	19
Florinda's Strange Pet	20
Strange Plants	21
Cactuses, Monsters, Lizards, and Scorpions	22
Creepy Crawlers	23
Animals, East and West	24
Feathered Flyers	25
Wild Flowers	26
A Flowering Business	27
Delicious Drinks	28
The Spider and the Baseball Player	29
How Old Am I?	30
How Long Can You Stand on One Foot?	31
Body Bones and Muscles	32
Answers	33

INTRODUCTION

What Is REACH?

Recently, there has been a tremendous surge of interest in the gifted student in mathematics. Most of the interest has been focused on the high school level. There have been few attempts to prepare curricula for the younger mathematically talented student.

REACH is a mathematics program designed specifically for gifted students in grades 2–8. Each of the seven books has a major theme and contains 32 pages of blackline masters designed to show application of mathematics to the sciences, social sciences, and to everyday living.

The books present a series of problems and activities that develop students' reasoning skills, computation facility and reading comprehension. Solving the problems requires finding information in displays; organizing data in lists, tables, and timelines; using deductive logic; guessing and checking; and performing a variety of computations.

The themes were selected based on knowledge of students' interests, and the science and social science curricula. Real events and data are used throughout the books. The level of computation in each book is consistent with the mathematics curriculum at that grade level. The reading level is at grade level or one year above.

What Is In REACH?

Chickabee Corners: THE COMMUNITY
The problems and activities in this book are designed to show applications of grade two arithmetic skills and concepts. Students will "reach out" into the community, travel down Main Street, and visit the police department, fire station, children's center, and several businesses including the plant shop, movie theater, and toy store.

Petunias, Potatoes, Pets, and People: LIVING THINGS
Students learn about the world of living things as they apply grade 3 computation skills to the solution of problems in this book. Among the adventures are: visits to a serpentarium and an aquarium; identifying animal tracks; reading about plants that eat insects; and getting the facts about the number of muscles and bones in their bodies.

Shows, Sports, Stumpers, and Stories: THAT'S ENTERTAINMENT
Students visit Disneyworld, see dynamic dolphins dance and whistle, solve the mystery of the missing marshmallow, try some number tricks, and learn about famous board games and types of puppets. And they apply grade 4 computation skills to the solution of these problems about entertainment.

Get the Message: COMMUNICATION
Students learn about different forms of communication, the history of communication, and communication networks in *Get the Message.* Among the topics are: Speaking in Space, Dits and Dahs (Morse code), Braille, Fast Talkers, Ringing Codes, Stop the Press, and Famous Photo Firsts. The computation level of this book is grade 5.

By Land, by Sea, by Air: TRANSPORTATION

Have you ever tried walking on your hands? Forms of transportation, aids to transportation, and the history of transportation provide the content of this book. Students apply grade 6 computation skills to the solution of stagecoach, map, space, raft, plane, taxi, train, bicycle, balloon, and automobile problems.

Headlines of the Past, Present and Future: WHAT'S THE NEWS?

Major events in the past, the present and the future provide the settings for the pages in this book. Students use grade 7 computation skills and solve problems about GOGO, a new computer language; Lindbergh's trans-Atlantic flight; the Susan B. Anthony dollar; the international Olympics; the world's largest pizza; and the successful implantation of an artificial heart.

Making Sense out of Cents: A QUESTION OF MONEY

Identifying the better buy, computing discounts, sorting out credit cards and checks, using coupons, and discovering how much money there is in a ton of nickels are some of the experiences in this book. Students apply grade 8 computation skills to a variety of money problems.

How REACH May Be Used

REACH is appropriate for use in a regular classroom or a classroom designated for gifted students. REACH broadens students' interests and knowledge while providing practice in problem solving and computation. The pages may be used as alternatives to classroom assignments, or may be used to augment the curriculum for advanced students who complete their regular assignments early. REACH pages provide ideal homework challenges as well.

The pages in each book are sequenced by difficulty, but need not be completed in order. For students who desire to REACH further, we suggest using the next level book.

A Trip to the Zoo

Peacock   **Lion**   **Deer**   **Elephant**

Stella, Martin, Orlando, and Karen went to the zoo.
They saw many animals.

Use the pictures and the clues to tell
which animal each child liked best.

1. The animal I liked best:
  • Does not have tusks.
  • Does not have feathers.
  • Has antlers.

  I liked the _____.

2. The animal I liked best:
  • Has 4 legs.
  • Does not have antlers.
  • Does not have a trunk.

  I liked the _____.

3. The animal I liked best:
  • Does not have a mane.
  • Does not have a trunk.
  • Is not a deer.

  I liked the _____.

4. The animal I liked best:
  • Does not have antlers.
  • Has 4 legs.
  • Has very big ears.

  I liked the _____.

1

Legs, Feet, and Toes

Make drawings to help you solve these problems.

> A **centipede** does not have 100 legs.
> It has 2 legs on each segment of its body.
> Most centipedes have 36 legs.

How many legs does each of these centipedes have?
Draw the legs to help you answer the question.

1. 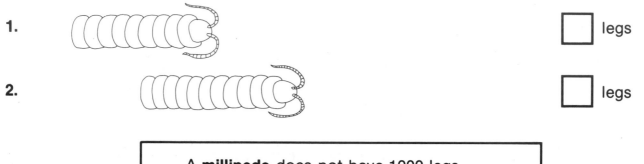 ☐ legs

2. ☐ legs

> A **millipede** does not have 1000 legs.
> It has 4 legs on each segment of its body.
> Some millipedes have 330 legs.

How many legs does each of these millipedes have? Draw the legs.

3. ☐ legs

4. ☐ legs

> **Prairie dogs** don't have the same number of
> toes on each foot.
> They have 4 toes on each of their front feet.
> They have 5 toes on each of their back feet.

5. How many toes does a prairie dog have? Draw the toes.

☐ toes.

Name _____

Dr. Doomuch's Pet Supplies

GIVE YOUR PET A TREAT!

Dog Brush	$4
Chew Toy	$3
Leash	$7
Cat Collar	$6
Fish Bowl	$10

Use the facts in the sign.
Tell what each person bought.

1. Antonio bought 2 items.
   He paid $11.

   Antonio bought a _____

   and a _____.

2. Ana bought 2 items at the sale.
   She paid $16.

   Ana bought a _____

   and a _____.

3. Jud had $15.
   He bought one item at the sale.
   He has $5 left.

   Jud bought a _____.

4. Mark had $10.
   He bought one item.
   He has $4 left.

   He bought a _____.

5. Martha bought 3 different items.
   She paid $14.

   She bought a _____,

   a _____, and a

   _____.

6. Laura spent $9 at the sale.
   She bought 3 items that were
   the same.

   Laura bought 3 _____.

Sweet Dreams

Some animals sleep for many months when it is cold.
This sleep is called hibernation.
These animals eat a lot of food in the fall.
They store the food in their bodies.
Then they do not have to eat when they are hibernating.

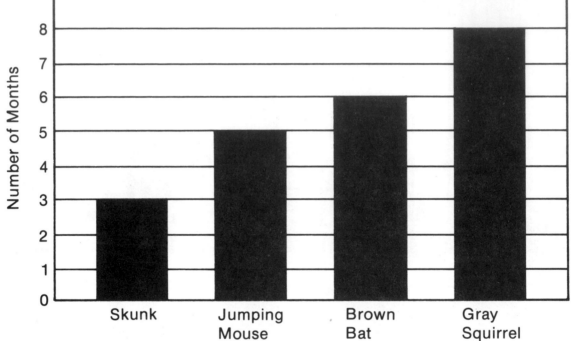

The bar graph shows how long some
animals hibernated in New England last year.
Use the graph to answer the questions.

1. Which animal hibernated for 5 months?

_____

2. Which animal hibernated the longest?

_____

How many months did it hibernate?

_____

3. Which animal hibernated the least?

_____

How many months did it hibernate?

_____

4. How many more months did the brown
bat hibernate than the jumping
mouse?

_____

5. How many less months did the skunk
hibernate than the gray squirrel?

_____

6. Which animal hibernated twice as long
as the skunk?

_____

Name _____

Bean's Story

Read "The Story of the Bean." The pictures tell the story.
But they are out of order. Put the pictures in order.
Put the letter of the first picture in the first box.
Put the letter of the second picture in the second box.
Do this for all of the pictures.
Did you spell 2 story words?

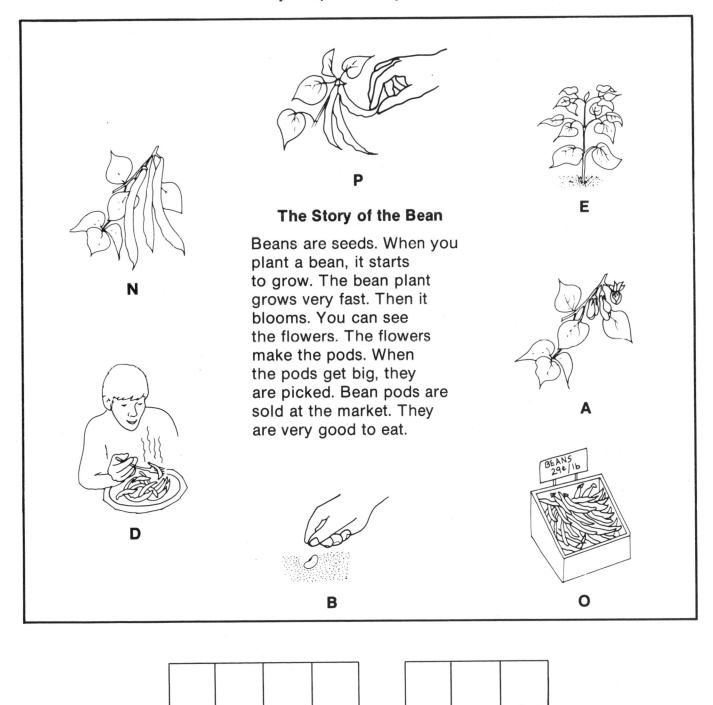

The Story of the Bean

Beans are seeds. When you plant a bean, it starts to grow. The bean plant grows very fast. Then it blooms. You can see the flowers. The flowers make the pods. When the pods get big, they are picked. Bean pods are sold at the market. They are very good to eat.

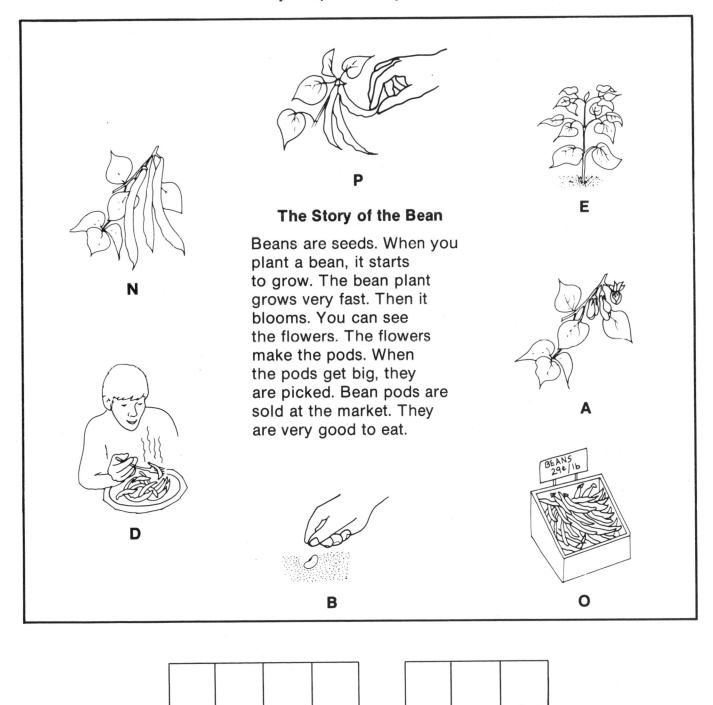

Vegetables, Fruits, and Vegetable-Fruits

Scientists say that certain foods we call vegetables are
really fruits! They are fruits because they have seeds.
We will call these foods VEGETABLE-FRUITS.

Use the clues and the lists to find what
each person ate.

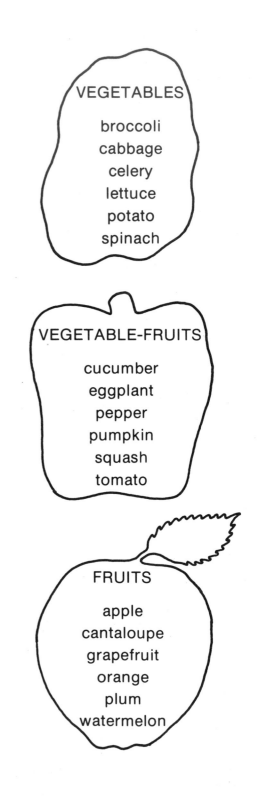

VEGETABLES

broccoli
cabbage
celery
lettuce
potato
spinach

1. Which VEGETABLE did Rachel have
for dinner?
- There are 2 *o*'s in its name.
- It is not a potato.

Rachel had _____.

VEGETABLE-FRUITS

cucumber
eggplant
pepper
pumpkin
squash
tomato

2. Which of these VEGETABLE-FRUITS
did Jody have for lunch?
- It does not begin with a *p*.
- There are less than 8 letters in
its name.
- It is not a tomato.

Jody had _____.

FRUITS

apple
cantaloupe
grapefruit
orange
plum
watermelon

3. Which FRUIT did Brett have for a
snack?
- There are more than 4 letters in
its name.
- There is an *n* in its name.
- It is larger than an orange.
- It is not a watermelon.

Brett had _____.

Harborside Aquarium

GIFT SHOP
SEA FLAG $ 2
WHALE POSTER $ 3
DIVING HANDBOOK $ 5
STRANGE FISH BOOK $ 7
THE OCEAN BOOK $ 9

Use the facts in the sign to solve the problems.

1. Anders spent $8.
   He bought 2 items.
   Anders bought

   _____ and _____.

2. Nancy spent $11.
   She bought 2 items.
   Nancy bought

   _____ and _____.

3. Sarah spent $15.
   She bought 3 different items.
   She bought

   _____, _____,

   and _____.

4. Billy spent $18.
   He bought 3 different items.
   Billy bought

   _____, _____,

   and _____.

5. Kara bought 2 whale posters and a
   Strange Fish book.
   How much money did she spend?

   _____

6. You can spend up to $12 in the gift
   shop.
   Make a list of the items you want to
   buy.
   Tell how much money you will spend
   in all.

ITEMS	COST
Total	

Tooth Totals

Animal	Number of Teeth
Billy Bat	38
Freddy Fox	42
Melissa Monkey	32
Polly Opossum	50
Ricky Raccoon	40
Roy Boy	20

The table shows the number of teeth for each animal. Use the table to answer the questions.

1. Which animal has 50 teeth?

_____

2. Does Billy Bat have more teeth than Ricky Raccoon?

_____

3. Freddy Fox said, "I have the same number of teeth as Beverly Bear." How many teeth does Beverly Bear have?

_____

4. How many more teeth does Freddy Fox have than Melissa Monkey?

_____

5. Which animal has 18 more teeth than Roy Boy?

_____

6. Roy Boy will have 12 more teeth when he grows up. How many teeth will Roy Boy have when he grows up?

_____

7. Which animal has 10 less teeth than Polly Opossum?

_____

8. Roy Boy has 10 teeth in his upper jaw. How many teeth does he have in his lower jaw?

_____

Birth of a Butterfly

Name _____

A mother monarch butterfly lays her egg on a leaf.
A small caterpillar hatches from the egg.
The caterpillar eats leaves. Then it hangs from a twig.

It forms a shell around itself.
The shell is called a chrysalis.
A butterfly comes out of the chrysalis.

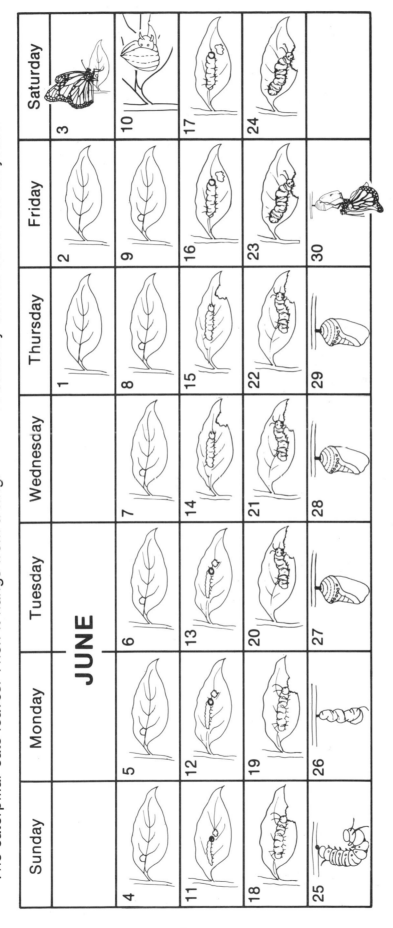

JUNE

Sunday	Monday	Tuesday	Wednesday	Thursday	Friday	Saturday
				1	2	3
4	5	6	7	8	9	10
11	12	13	14	15	16	17
18	19	20	21	22	23	24
25	26	27	28	29	30	

Use the calendar to help you answer the questions.

1. On which day of the week did the mother monarch lay the egg? _____

2. How many days after the egg was laid did the caterpillar hatch from the egg? _____

3. On which date did the caterpillar hatch from the egg? _____

4. For how many days did the caterpillar eat leaves? _____

5. On which day of the week did the caterpillar hang from the twig? _____

6. On which day of the week did the butterfly come out of the chrysalis? _____

7. How many days after the egg was laid did the butterfly come out of the chrysalis? _____

Moving Up

AGE	HEIGHTS (in centimeters)	
	Sean	Monica
Birth	50	50
1 year	76	74
5 years	110	109
8 years	127	127
12 years	149	151
18 years	177	164

The table shows the children's heights at different ages. Use the table to answer the questions.

1. At what age was Monica taller than Sean?

_____

How much taller was she?

_____

2. At what age was Monica 1 centimeter shorter than Sean?

_____

3. How much taller was Sean than Monica when they were 1 year old?

_____

4. How much taller was Sean than Monica when they were 18 years old?

_____

5. How many centimeters did Sean grow from age 8 to age 12?

_____

6. How many centimeters did Monica grow from age 8 to age 18?

_____

10

Big Ocean Animals

Jess, Mia, and Dave each read about an ocean animal.

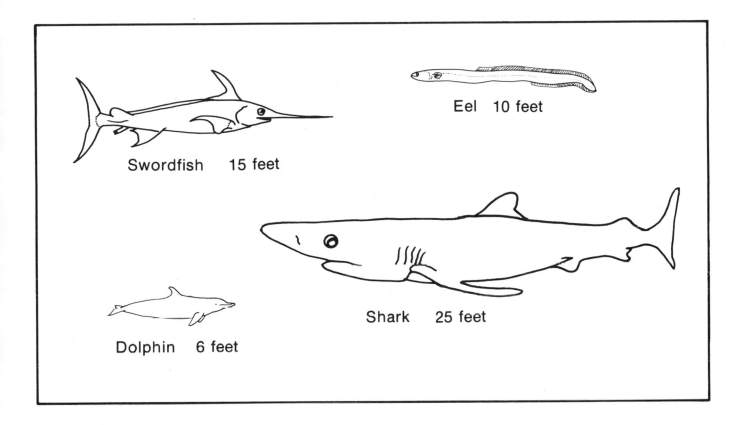

Swordfish   15 feet

Eel   10 feet

Shark   25 feet

Dolphin   6 feet

Use the clues to name the animals.

1. • Jess's animal is longer than 6 feet.
   • The first letter in its name is an *s*.
   • It is not a swordfish.

   Jess read about a _____.

2. • Mia's animal is not 25 feet long.
   • It is less than 15 feet long.
   • There is an *h* in its name.

   Mia read about a _____.

3. • Dave's animal is less than 25 feet long.
   • There are more than 4 letters in its name.
   • There is an *r* in its name.

   Dave read about a _____.

11

Class Pet

Mr. Lovebird's class wanted a hamster.
The students earned $35. They went to the pet store.

HAMSTERS
GOLDEN $ 5
FANCY $ 6
RUSSIAN $ 9

SUPPLIES
CAGE $ 16
WATER BOTTLE $ 2
RUNNING WHEEL $ 8
FOOD $ 2

Use the sign to answer the students' questions.

1. John asked, "How much would one golden hamster and one Russian hamster cost altogether?"

   _____

2. Melinda asked, "How much would a cage and a box of food cost?"

   _____

3. Ramon asked, "How much would it cost for a Russian hamster and a running wheel?"

   _____

4. Laurette asked, "How much would it cost to buy a fancy hamster, a cage, and a water bottle?"

   _____

5. Sandra said, "I think we should buy a Russian hamster and a cage. How much would we have left from our $35?"

   _____

6. Paul said, "We have $35. How much would we have left if we bought a fancy hamster and a box of food?"

   _____

Snake Facts

A serpentarium is a zoo for snakes.
At the Snakeside Serpentarium you may see these snakes.

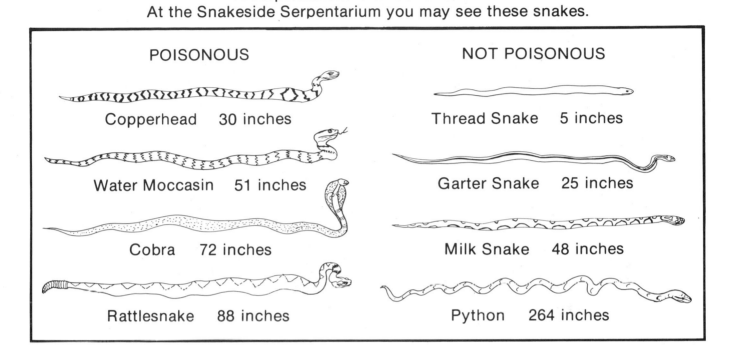

POISONOUS

Copperhead   30 inches

Water Moccasin   51 inches

Cobra   72 inches

Rattlesnake   88 inches

NOT POISONOUS

Thread Snake   5 inches

Garter Snake   25 inches

Milk Snake   48 inches

Python   264 inches

Use the facts in the pictures to solve the problems.

1. The water moccasin and the garter snake live in the United States. How many inches longer is the water moccasin than the garter snake?

   _____

2. The copperhead has a copper-colored head. How many inches shorter than the python is the copperhead?

   _____

3. The rattlesnake and the milk snake live in the United States. The rattlesnake has a rattle on the end of its tail. How many inches longer is the rattlesnake than the milk snake?

   _____

4. The shortest adult snake in the world is the thread snake. It lives in the Caribbean Islands. How many inches shorter is the thread snake than the water moccasin?

   _____

5. The python is the longest of all snakes. Pythons live in Asia and Africa. How many inches longer is the python than the garter snake?

   _____

6. The cobra lives in Africa and Asia. The king cobra is the largest cobra. It is about the length of 3 of the cobras shown in the picture. About how many inches long is the king cobra?

   _____

The One Minute Race

The animals had a race.
The table shows how far each animal ran in one minute.

ANIMAL	DISTANCE (in feet)
Charlie Cheetah	5280
Harry Horse	3500
Morris Man	1320
Perry Pig	750

Use the table to help you answer
the questions.

1. Which animal ran the farthest?

_____

2. How many feet did Morris Man run?

_____

3. How many feet farther did Harry Horse
run than Morris Man?

_____

4. How many feet farther did Charlie
Cheetah run than Peggy Pig?

_____

Use the clues to name the animals.

5. • I ran farther than the pig.
   • I didn't run as far as the cheetah.
   • I am not Morris Man.

   I am _____.

6. • I ran more than 800 feet.
   • I ran less than 5000 feet.
   • I am not a horse.

   I am _____.

14

Keep Track of the Animal Tracks

You make tracks with your feet and shoes.
Animals make tracks with their feet.

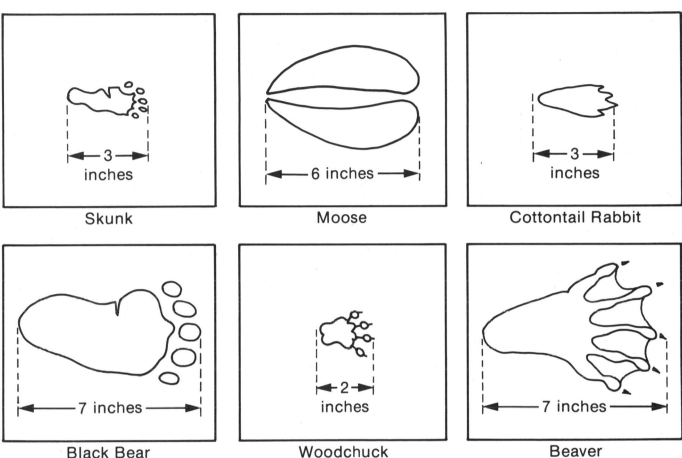

3 inches	6 inches	3 inches
Skunk	Moose	Cottontail Rabbit
7 inches	2 inches	7 inches
Black Bear	Woodchuck	Beaver

Use the pictures and the clues to name the animals.

1. Which animal am I?
 • My track is more than 4 inches long.
 • I am not a beaver.
 • I do not have toes.

  I am a _____.

2. Which animal am I?
 • My track is longer than a woodchuck's track.
 • It is less than 6 inches.
 • I have 5 toes.

  I am a _____.

3. Which animal am I?
 • My track is shorter than a moose's track.
 • It is longer than a woodchuck's track.
 • I am not a skunk.

  I am a _____.

4. Which animal am I?
 • I have 5 toes.
 • My track is longer than a skunk's track.
 • I am not a black bear.

  I am a _____.

Food for a Giant

Mr. Thompson took his class to the state fair.
They saw giant fruits and vegetables.

Read and answer the questions.

1. Derick saw a giant bean pod. It was 6 inches longer than Derick's shoe. His shoe was 7 inches long. How long was the bean pod?

   _____

2. Freddy saw 2 big potatoes. One potato weighed 16 pounds. The other potato weighed 15 pounds. How much did the potatoes weigh together?

   _____

3. Rhonda saw a cucumber that was 62 inches long. She saw a pepper that was 13 inches long. How much longer was the cucumber than the pepper?

   _____

4. Regina saw a cabbage that weighed 153 pounds. She saw a celery stalk that weighed 19 pounds. How much more did the cabbage weigh than the celery?

   _____

5. Jill saw a watermelon that weighed 170 pounds. She said, "That watermelon weighs 100 pounds more than I do!" How much does Jill weigh?

   _____

6. Troy saw a squash that weighed 153 pounds. Brenda saw a squash that weighed 166 pounds more than the one that Troy saw. What was the weight of the squash that Brenda saw?

   _____

Tree Time

Ms. Arigo's class read stories about trees.

Solve the problems.

1. Gilberto read a story about a California redwood tree and a Douglas fir tree. The California redwood tree was 350 feet tall. The Douglas fir tree was 250 feet tall. How much taller was the redwood tree than the fir tree?

   _____

2. Richard read a book about an orange tree in Florida. The first orange grew when the tree was 5 years old. Oranges grew on the tree every year until it was 55 years old. How many years did oranges grow on the tree?

   _____

3. Isabel learned that maple syrup is made from the sap of a maple tree. At the Vermont Maple Syrup Center 40 gallons of sap are used to make one gallon of syrup. How many gallons of sap are used to make 2 gallons of syrup?

   _____

4. Jon read about 2 nut trees. The pecan tree was 120 feet tall. The black walnut tree was 90 feet tall. How much taller was the pecan tree than the walnut tree?

   _____

5. Carol's book had pictures of leaves. The tulip tree leaf was 5 inches long. The black locust leaf was 14 inches long. How much longer was the black locust leaf than the tulip tree leaf?

   _____

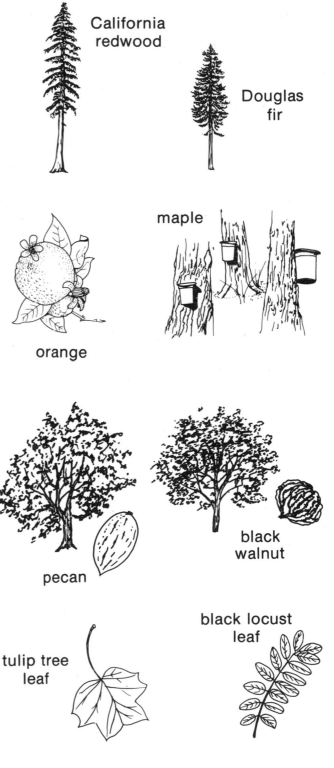

California redwood

Douglas fir

maple

orange

pecan

black walnut

black locust leaf

tulip tree leaf

17

Free Ride

Some animals carry their babies. The opossum, the kangaroo, and the koala carry their babies in pouches.

Solve the problems.

1. This opossum is carrying 9 babies. Five of the babies are on her back. The others are in her pouch. How many babies are in her pouch?

_____

2. A newborn opossum is about 1 centimeter long. A newborn kangaroo is about 1 centimeter longer than a newborn opossum. About how long is a newborn kangaroo?

_____ centimeters

3. Young kangaroos are called joeys. This joey is 12 centimeters tall. This mother kangaroo is 194 centimeters tall. How much taller is the mother than her joey?

_____ centimeters

4. Joeys are carried in their mothers' pouches until they are about 7 months old. This kangaroo took her joey for a jumping ride. She jumped 4 meters. Then she jumped 6 meters. Then she jumped 5 meters. How many meters did she jump in all?

_____ meters

5. A koala is a small animal that lives in Australia. It looks like a teddy bear. This mother koala was 3 centimeters long when she was born. She is now 60 centimeters longer. How long is this mother koala now?

_____ centimeters

6. The mother koala carried her babies in her pouch until they were 6 months old. The mother opossum carried her babies in her pouch until they were 2 months old. How many more months did the koala carry her babies than did the opossum?

_____

Barry Brontosaurus and His Friends

Barry, Terry, Cory, Danny, and Spike are dinosaurs.
They lived millions of years ago.

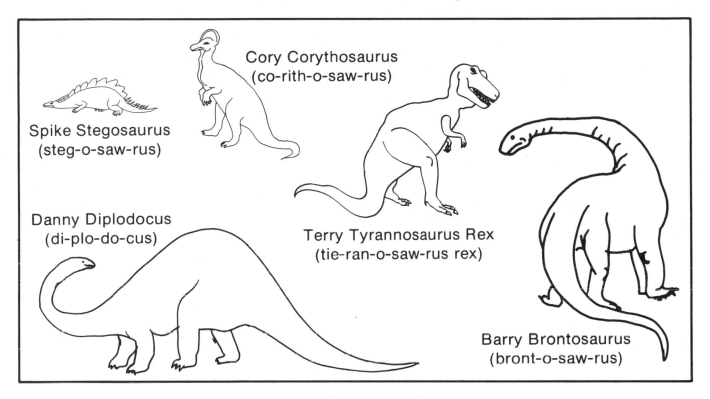

Spike Stegosaurus
(steg-o-saw-rus)

Cory Corythosaurus
(co-rith-o-saw-rus)

Danny Diplodocus
(di-plo-do-cus)

Terry Tyrannosaurus Rex
(tie-ran-o-saw-rus rex)

Barry Brontosaurus
(bront-o-saw-rus)

Solve the problems.

1. Barry was 24 meters long.
Terry was 12 meters long.
How much longer was Barry than
Terry?

_____ meters.

2. Danny Diplodocus was the largest of
the dinosaurs. He was 3 meters longer
than Barry. Barry was 24 meters long.
How long was Danny?

_____ meters.

3. Terry was 12 meters long.
Cory was 3 meters shorter than Terry.
How long was Cory?

_____ meters.

4. Spike's head was 40 centimeters long.
His body and tail were 560 centimeters
long. How long was Spike?

_____ centimeters.

5. Barry's brain weighed 450 grams.
Spike's brain weighed 70 grams. How
much more did Barry's brain weigh
than Spike's brain?

_____ grams.

6. Barry weighed 27 metric tons. Cory
weighed 6 metric tons. How many
more metric tons did Barry weigh than
Cory?

_____ metric tons.

Florinda's Strange Pet

Florinda wrote a story about her strange pet.
Read the story and answer the questions.

My name is Florinda.
I have a pet dinosaur named Dino.

He has 4 legs. There are 24 spots on his legs. There are the same number of spots on each leg. The spots are red or green or purple or orange.

Dino is ticklish. When he is tickled he laughs and opens one of his 3 giant mouths. He uses one of his other mouths for eating. He uses his third mouth for singing. There are 8 teeth in each mouth.

One day, Dino sang 8 short songs before breakfast. Then he ate 16 mushy bananas and 7 sour grapes. After breakfast he sang 5 silly songs. His favorite silly song is about a happy red monster named Harpy.

1. How many spots does Dino have on each leg?

_____

2. How many teeth does Dino have altogether?

_____

3. How many more bananas did Dino eat than grapes?

_____

4. How many pieces of fruit did Dino eat altogether?

_____

5. How many songs did Dino sing in all?

_____

6. How many more songs did Dino sing before breakfast than after breakfast?

_____

Name _____

Strange Plants

Did you ever see a plant eat an insect?
These plants eat insects!

PITCHER PLANT

VENUS'S FLYTRAP

SUNDEW

Use the clues to solve the problems.

1. Draw a line from the name of the plant to the picture.

   CLUES
   • The sundew has drops on its needles.
   • The pitcher plant looks like a pitcher.

3. Which plant caught the grasshopper?

   CLUES
   • The grasshopper hopped away from the Venus's flytrap.
   • The grasshopper was not caught by the plant with needles.

   The _____ caught the fly.

2. Which plant caught the fly?

   CLUES
   • The fly did not get caught in the pitcher plant.
   • The fly was not caught by a plant with drops on its needles.

   The _____ caught the fly.

Cactuses, Monsters, Lizards, and Scorpions

A desert is a hot, dry place. It gets very little rain.
Special plants and animals live in the desert.

Use the pictures to help solve the problems.

1. How tall is the cactus? _____ feet

2. Hans is standing near the cactus.

How tall is Hans? _____ feet

3. How much taller is the cactus than Hans?

_____ feet

4. This cactus is 199 years old. Hans is 12 years old. How many years older is the cactus than Hans?

_____ years

5. The Gila monster is a lizard that lives in the desert. This Gila monster is 16 inches long. How long is its tail?

_____ inches

6. The leopard lizard lives near the giant cactus. It is 4 inches shorter than the Gila monster. How long is this leopard lizard?

_____ inches

7. The scorpion's tail is as long its body. This scorpion is 4 inches long from end to end. How long is this scorpion's tail?

_____ inches

The giant cactus grows in the desert. It has sharp spines. It grows very tall. It lives a long time.

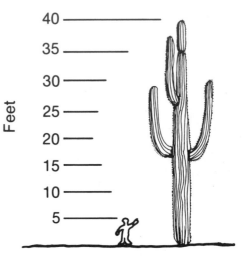

Feet: 40, 35, 30, 25, 20, 15, 10, 5

Gila monster

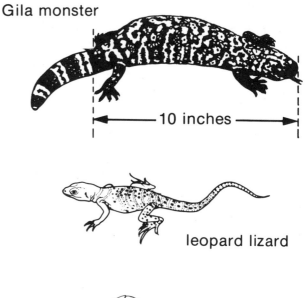

10 inches

leopard lizard

scorpion

Name _____

Creepy Crawlers

An insect has 6 legs. Its body has 3 parts.
Some insects have wings. An ant is an insect.
A bee is an insect.

A spider is not an insect.
It has 8 legs. Its body has 2 parts.

Use the facts in the story to answer the questions.

Ant

Bee

1. How many more legs does a spider have than an ant?

_____

2. How many more parts does a bee's body have than a spider's body?

_____

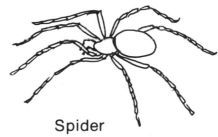

Spider

Thad collects creepy crawlers.
He found 9 ants, 7 bees, and 6 spiders.

3. How many insects did Thad find?

_____

4. How many insects and spiders did Thad find altogether?

_____

5. How many more ants than spiders did Thad find?

_____

Liz collects creepy crawlers.
She found 3 ants, 5 bees, and 8 spiders.

6. How many insects did Liz find?

_____

7. How many insects and spiders did Liz find altogether?

_____

8. Liz counted the legs on her ants. How many ant legs did she count in all?

_____

Animals, East and West

The map shows some animals that live in the United States.

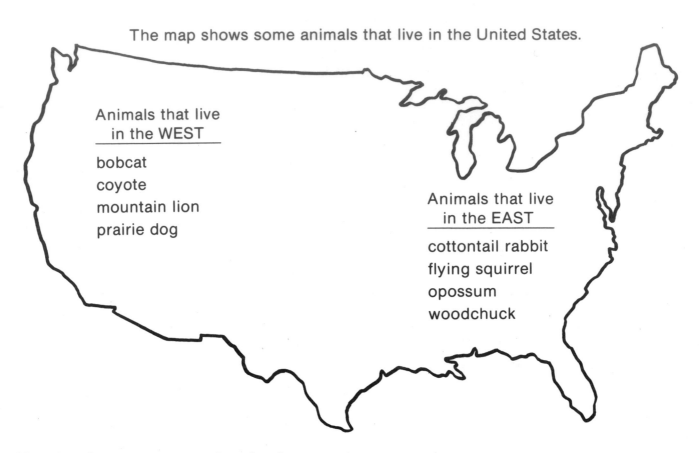

Animals that live
  in the WEST
_____

bobcat
coyote
mountain lion
prairie dog

Animals that live
  in the EAST
_____

cottontail rabbit
flying squirrel
opossum
woodchuck

Use the clues to name each animal.

1. Katie read about an animal in a science book.
  - This animal lives in the East.
  - There is one word in its name.
  - This animal's name does not end with a *k*.

Katie read about _____.

2. Marcy saw a picture of an animal in a book.
  - This animal lives in the West.
  - There are 2 words in its name.
  - This animal does not have a *u* in its name.

Marcy saw a picture of

_____.

3. José saw an animal in the woods.
  - This animal lives in the East.
  - This animal's name does not begin with a *c*.
  - This animal has a two-word name.

José saw _____.

4. Sal saw a movie about an animal.
  - This animal lives in the West.
  - There are 2 *o*'s in its name.
  - There is one word in its name.

Sal saw a movie about

_____.

Feathered Flyers

Penny and Cliff visited an aviary. An aviary is
a very large cage for birds. Penny and Cliff walked through
the aviary and saw many different kinds of birds.

Solve the problems.

1. Reggie the road runner ran by Penny
and Cliff. Reggie was 22 inches long.
His head and body were 11 inches
long. How long was Reggie's tail?

_____

2. Penny saw Carrie the canary and Sheri
the swan. Carrie was 10 years old.
Sheri was 15 years older than Carrie.
How old was Sheri?

_____

3. Penny said, "Let's go to see some
birds' eggs." Rosy the robin had laid 4
eggs. Clara the quail had laid 11 more
eggs than Rosy. How many eggs had
Clara laid?

_____

4. Penny and Cliff saw 2 big ostrich
eggs. Each egg weighed about
3 pounds. About how many pounds
did the eggs weigh altogether?

_____

5. Cliff saw Pete the pelican. He also saw
Cal the California condor. Pete's wings
were 110 inches from tip to tip. Cal's
wings were 10 inches longer than
Pete's. How long were Cal's wings?

_____

6. Penny and Cliff learned that about 35
thousand bald eagles live in Alaska
and 4 thousand bald eagles live in the
other states. About how many bald
eagles live in the United States?

_____

Wild Flowers

Read the stories about the wild flowers.
Then solve the problems.

The **buttercup** is the color of butter. It is sometimes called a crowfoot because its leaf looks like a crow's foot. Color the buttercup.

The **johnny-jump-up** looks like a pansy. Its petals are blue, purple, or yellow. It seems to jump-up or grow everywhere. Color the johnny-jump-ups.

The **day lilies** grow in fields. The flower is only open during the daytime. The day lily is orange or yellow. Color the day lily.

1. Jane counted johnny-jump-up flowers in the woods. She counted 4 blue flowers, 3 yellow flowers, and 2 purple flowers. How many flowers did Jane count in all?

   _____

2. Peg saw 12 day lilies. Three of the lilies were yellow. How many of the lilies were not yellow?

   _____

3. Tim gave 10 buttercups to Brenda. He gave 12 buttercups to Lynn. How many buttercups did Tim give away?

   _____

4. Mr. Blake bought 12 day lilies. He gave all of the lilies to his 3 children. They all got the same number of lilies. How many did each child receive?

   _____

5. Rita drew a picture of 3 vases of flowers. There were 3 wild flowers in each vase. How many wild flowers did Rita draw?

   _____

26

A Flowering Business

Mrs. Larsen grows and sells pots and boxes
of flowers. The table shows the number of pots
and boxes she has for sale.

Use the facts in the table to answer the
questions.

| Flowers | Number of | |
	Pots	Boxes
Marigolds	12	45
Petunias	30	33
Daisies	25	75
Pansies	15	60

1. How many more boxes of daisies does
Mrs. Larsen have than pots of daisies?

_____

2. How many more boxes of daisies does
Mrs. Larsen have than boxes of
marigolds?

_____

3. Mrs. Larsen had 225 pansies. She
planted 180 pansies in boxes. She
planted the other pansies in pots. How
many pansies did Mrs. Larsen plant in
pots?

_____

4. There are 24 marigolds in each box.
The marigolds are in 3 rows. There are
the same number of marigolds in each
row. How many marigolds are in each
row?

_____

6. How many pots of flowers does Mrs.
Larsen have altogether?

_____

5. Mrs. Larsen planted 2 petunias in each
pot. How many petunias did she plant
in the pots altogether?

_____

7. How many boxes of flowers does Mrs.
Larsen have in all?

_____

Delicious Drinks

It is easy to make drinks from fresh fruit.
Fresh fruit drinks are healthy and they taste good.

Solve the problems.

1. Gary uses the juice from one grapefruit to make 2 glasses of grapefruit juice. How many grapefruits does Gary use to make 6 glasses of grapefruit juice?

_____

2. Oliver uses 5 oranges to make one glass of orange juice. How many oranges does Oliver use to make 4 glasses of orange juice?

_____

3. Barbara wants to make 4 cups of banana milk shake. How many cups of milk will she need?

_____

4. Brian has 4 cups of milk and 8 bananas. How many cups of banana milk shake can he make?

_____

5. Pedro wants to make 6 cups of pineapple-banana shake. How many bananas will he need?

_____

6. Patty has 6 cups of pineapple juice and 6 sliced bananas. How many cups of pineapple-banana shake can she make?

_____

BANANA MILK SHAKE

1 cup milk
2 bananas

Blend until smooth.
Makes 2 cups.

PINEAPPLE-BANANA SHAKE

2 cups pineapple juice
2 sliced bananas

Blend until smooth.
Makes 3 cups.

The Spider and the Baseball Player

WHY ARE SPIDERS GOOD BASEBALL PLAYERS?

You can solve this riddle.

Here's how:

Do each problem.
Match the letter in each box with the answer below.

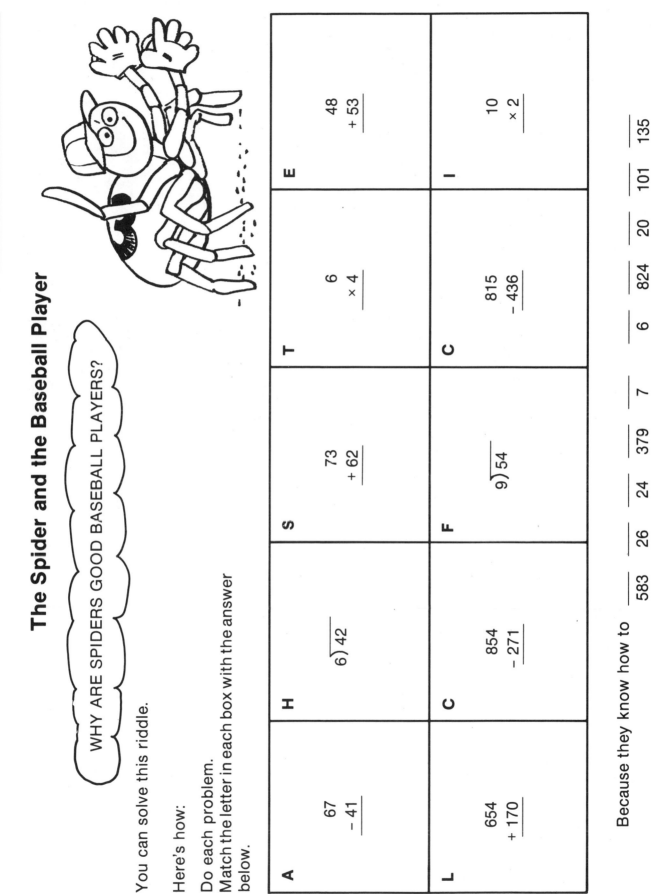

A	H	S	E
67 − 41	6)‾42	73 + 62	48 + 53

C	T	I
	6 × 4	10 × 2

L	C	F
654 + 170	815 − 436	9)‾54

Because they know how to

___ ___ ___ ___ ___ ___ ___ ___ ___ ___
583 26   24 379   7   6   824   20 101 135

How Old Am I?

Debbie

_____ years

Jeff

_____ years

Norma

_____ years

Ben

_____ years

Tina

_____ years

Eric

_____ years

Use the facts. Find the age of each person.
Write the age under the name.

1. Ben's age
  - is less than 20.
  - is greater than 10.
  - is a number you say when you count by 5's.

2. Debbie is 3 years younger than Ben.

3. Debbie is 2 years older than Eric.

4. If you add 10 to Eric's age, you get Tina's age.

5. Norma is 7 years younger than Ben.

6. Jeff's age is less than 15. Jeff is older than Debbie. Jeff is not 14 years old.

Check: The sum of the ages is 78.

How Long Can You Stand on One Foot?

Jan, Carl, and Maria read about these world records.

WORLD RECORDS	TIME WITHOUT STOPPING
Game of hopscotch	_____
Telling jokes	_____
Singing	153 hours
Talking (men)	150 hours
Talking (women)	_____
Spinning a yo-yo	_____
Clapping hands	_____
Standing on one foot	_____

Solve the problems. Use the answers to fill in the times in the table.

1. Jan and Carl played hopscotch for 2 hours. The world's longest game of hopscotch is 70 hours longer than Jan and Carl's game. How many hours is the world's longest game of hopscotch?

   _____

2. The record for telling jokes is 129 hours less than the record for singing. What is the record for telling jokes without stopping?

   _____

3. The world record for talking without stopping for women is 40 hours less than for men. What is the women's record?

   _____

4. The world record for spinning a yo-yo is 20 hours more than 100 hours. How many hours is the yo-yo record?

   _____

5. Jan clapped her hands for 35 minutes without stopping. The world record is 2545 minutes longer than Jan's time. What is the world record for clapping hands?

   _____

6. Carl tried to stand on one foot. He did it for 2 minutes. The world record is 1978 minutes longer than Carl's time. What is the world record for standing on one foot?

   _____

TRY THIS: Time yourself. How many minutes can you stand on one foot?

Name _____

Body Bones and Muscles

Our bodies have muscles and bones.
They work together to help us move.

Use the clues to find the answers. Draw a
ring around the answer in the sign.

1. How many bones are in your foot?
   • The number of bones is less than 27.
   • The number does not have a 1 in it.
   • The number is not 4 x 5.

26	29
21	20

2. How many muscles move the toes in
   your foot?
   • The number of muscles is less
     than 32.
   • The number is greater than 21.
   • The number is not 3 x 9.

57	16
24	27

3. How many bones are in one of your
   hands?
   • The number of bones does not have
     a 4 in it.
   • The number is greater than 21.
   • The number is not 15 + 11.

20	24
26	27

4. How many bones are in your head?
   • The number of bones is less than 28.
   • The number does not have a 6 in it.
   • The number is not 6 x 4.

28		21
	24	
26		36

5. How many muscles move your head?
   • The number of muscles is less than
     5 x 7.
   • The number is greater than 28 – 3.
   • The number is not 18 + 10.

46		28
	32	
23		25

ANSWERS

page 1: 1) deer   2) lion   3) peacock   4) elephant

page 2: 1) 18 legs   2) 22 legs   3) 24 legs   4) 36 legs   5) 18 toes

page 3: 1) A dog brush and a leash   2) A cat collar and a fish bowl   3) A fish
bowl   4) A cat collar   5) A dog brush, a chew toy, and a leash
6) Chew toys

page 4: 1) Jumping mouse   2) Gray squirrel; 8 months   3) Skunk; 3 months
4) 1 month   5) 5 months   6) Brown bat

page 5: BEAN POD

page 6: 1) Broccoli   2) Squash   3) Cantaloupe

page 7: 1) A whale poster and a *Diving Handbook*
2) A sea flag and a *The Ocean* book
3) A whale poster, a *Diving Handbook,* and a *Strange Fish* book
4) A sea flag, a *Strange Fish* book, and *The Ocean* book
5) $13
6) Answers will vary.

page 8: 1) Polly Opossum   2) No   3) 42 teeth   4) 10 teeth   5) Billy Bat
6) 32 teeth   7) Ricky Raccoon   8) 10 teeth

page 9: 1) Saturday   2) 7 days   3) June 10   4) 14 days   5) Sunday
6) Friday   7) 27 days

page 10: 1) 12 years; 2 centimeters   2) 5 years   3) 2 centimeters
4) 13 centimeters   5) 22 centimeters   6) 37 centimeters

page 11: 1) Shark   2) Dolphin   3) Swordfish

page 12: 1) $14   2) $18   3) $17   4) $24   5) $10   6) $27

page 13: 1) 26 inches   2) 234 inches   3) 40 inches   4) 46 inches
5) 239 inches   6) 216 inches

page 14: 1) Charlie Cheetah   2) 1320 feet   3) 2180 feet   4) 4530 feet
5) Harry Horse   6) Morris Man

page 15: 1) Moose   2) Skunk   3) Cottontail Rabbit   4) Beaver

page 16: 1) 13 inches   2) 31 pounds   3) 49 inches   4) 134 pounds
5) 70 pounds   6) 319 pounds

page 17: 1) 100 feet   2) 50 years   3) 80 gallons   4) 30 feet   5) 9 inches

page 18: 1) 4 babies   2) 2 centimeters   3) 182 centimeters   4) 15 meters
5) 63 centimeters   6) 4 months

page 19: 1) 12 meters   2) 27 meters   3) 9 meters   4) 600 centimeters
5) 380 grams   6) 21 metric tons

page 20: 1) 6 spots   2) 24 teeth   3) 9 bananas   4) 23 pieces of fruit
5) 13 songs   6) 3 songs

page 21: 2) Venus's Flytrap   3) Pitcher Plant

page 22: 1) 40 feet   2) 5 feet   3) 35 feet   4) 187 years   5) 6 inches
6) 12 inches   7) 2 inches

page 23: 1) 2 legs   2) 1 part   3) 16 insects   4) 22 insects and spiders
5) 3 ants   6) 8 insects   7) 16 insects and spiders   8) 18 legs

page 24: 1) an opossum   2) a prairie dog   3) a flying squirrel   4) a coyote

page 25: 1) 11 inches   2) 25 years old   3) 15 eggs   4) 6 pounds
5) 120 inches   6) 39 thousand

page 26: 1) 9 flowers   2) 9 day lilies   3) 22 buttercups   4) 4 day lilies
5) 9 wild flowers

page 27: 1) 50 boxes   2) 30 boxes   3) 45 pansies   4) 8 marigolds
5) 60 petunias   6) 82 pots   7) 213 boxes

page 28: 1) 3 grapefruits   2) 20 oranges   3) 2 cups of milk   4) 8 cups
5) 4 bananas   6) 9 cups

page 29: A = 26; H = 7; S = 135; T = 24; E = 101; L = 824; C = 583; F = 6; C = 379; I = 20
CATCH FLIES

page 30: 1) 15 years   2) 12 years   3) 10 years   4) 20 years   5) 8 years
6) 13 years

page 31: 1) 72 hours   2) 24 hours   3) 110 hours   4) 120 hours
5) 2580 minutes   6) 1980 minutes

page 32: 1) 26 bones   2) 24 muscles   3) 27 bones   4) 21 bones
5) 32 muscles